JOSEPH HAYDN

# QUARTET

for 2 Violins, Viola and Violoncello
D major/D-Dur/Ré majeur
Hob. III: 79
(Op. 76/5)

## Ernst Eulenburg Ltd
London · Mainz · Madrid · New York · Paris · Tokyo · Toronto · Zürich

# Quartet, No 79

## I

Josef Haydn, Op.76. No 5
1732-1809

E. E. 1157

Ernst Eulenburg Ltd

4

6

110

II

Largo. Cantabile e mesto

# III

Menuetto. Allegro

16

Monuetto D. C.

IV

Finale. Presto

V. E. 1157

22

E. E. 1157